Published 2015 by Geddes & Grosset, an imprint of The Gresham
Publishing Company Ltd, Academy Park, Building 4000,
Gower Street, Glasgow, G51 1PR, Scotland

ISBN 978-1-910680-63-6

Printed and bound in Malaysia

3 4 5 6 7 8 9 10

Toys

Judy Hamilton

Illustrated by Sue King

Tarantula
EARLY LEARNERS

Come and see my toys!
Some of them are very noisy!
This is my drum.

I also have a trumpet.

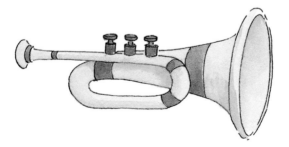

And this is my shaker — look!
I made it with a treacle tin and some rice!

Some of my toys are good for quiet times,
when I am inside the house:
I have books to look at

and I have some puzzles to do.

And my Mum made two sock puppets for me — one for each hand!

Toys can make bathtime lots of fun!
My big tap really works —

but my boat sometimes sinks!

Plastic cups and bottles are great toys for sloshing around in the bath!

Some of my toys are too big for the house.
I play with them in the garden on sunny days.
This is the slide.

Here is the sandpit.

And look at my tent! Isn't it a good idea!

There are other toys outside that give me lots of exercise:
I have a colourful tricycle.

This is the climbing frame.

And this is my special cardboard-box tunnel!

Some of my toys are building toys:
Old boxes can make great buildings!

These bricks stick together.

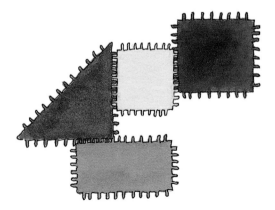

These bricks balance on top of each other.
Watch out! They are going to fall!

Some of my toys are good for sharing with friends:

Look at the cars on the road mat.

Football is always fun!

And this is the house in the corner of my bedroom!

This is my apron for helping with the washing-up.

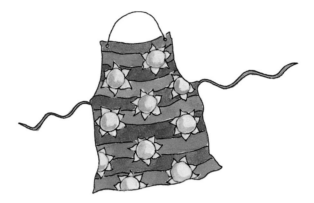

Here is a rolling pin for baking.

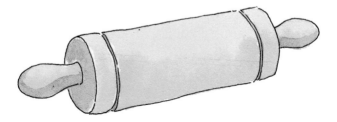

And this is my very own trowel for helping in the garden!

Here are some toys for making pictures:
Chunky coloured crayons make bright
pictures.

Sloshy paints make wet pictures!

And this roll of wallpaper is going to make the biggest picture ever!

Toys can help you to play pretending games:
Look at the cooker for playing houses.

Old hats and clothes are great fun for dressing up!

And this is my doctor's set.
Open your mouth wide and say "Ah!"

Cuddly toys are nice and soft to snuggle up to:

Here is my teddy.

This is my gorilla.

And this is the Humpty Dumpty that Granny made for me. Isn't his bow tie smart!

I like all my toys, but these are my favourites:

I love jumping on my beanbag.

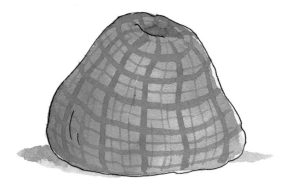

I can carry so many things in my trolley.

And my patchy old panda sleeps with me
every night in bed!

I hope you like my toys! Goodnight!

Birthday Surprise

It was the morning of Fireman Sam's birthday. When the post arrived, there were no cards for him, not even one from Sarah and James. Sam felt a bit sad.

Fireman Sam's friends hadn't really forgotten his birthday. They had lots of cards and presents for him and were planning a secret surprise party that afternoon in the Fire Station gym!

Norman was given the important job of keeping Sam away from the Fire Station until one o'clock.

Bella was in her café, decorating Sam's birthday cake, when Norman arrived with some candles.

"Take extra care with them because Mam says…" he said.

"Mamma mia!" said Bella. "Shh! Sam is-a coming!"

Bella hid the cake and Norman said, "Hi Sam, er, where are you going?"

"Hello, Norman," said Sam. "I'm off to the Fire Station."

"Oh, no, you're not!" thought Norman, and he ran ahead of Fireman Sam, to the park.
He threw a stick for Dusty into the fountain just as Sam walked by.

"Dusty's in the fountain and he can't swim!" cried Norman.

Suddenly, Dusty leapt out of
the fountain knocking Norman
into the water!
"I thought Dusty was in
the fountain," said Sam.

"He was," said Norman.
"But I ... er ... rescued him!"

Sam helped Norman out of the fountain and they walked towards the Fire Station.

But when they got there, Elvis was at the entrance.

"I'm afraid you can't come in, Sam," said Elvis.

"Why not?" asked Sam.

"Because you've got … to say the password!" said Norman.

"Er, that's right," said Elvis. "Special security, see."

"But I don't know the password,"
said Sam, looking confused.

"You could guess,"
suggested Norman.

Sam sighed.
"Oh, all right. 'Fountain'?"

"No," said Elvis, shaking
his head.

Whilst Sam carried on guessing,
Norman slipped inside.

"Sam's coming!" he cried.

"Put everything in the gym!" said
Sarah, grabbing the decorations.

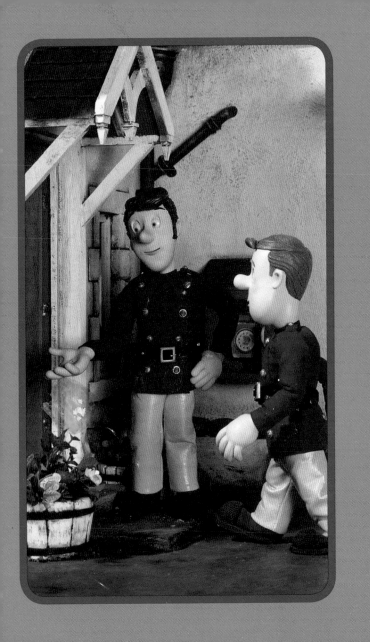

Norman went back outside.

"Is the password 'Dusty'?" guessed Sam.

"Correct!" said Elvis.
"Come in, Sam."

"Oh, no!" said Norman.
It was still too soon for Sam to go into the gym. Norman had to do something – quickly!

"Oo-er …" he said, going all wobbly. "I feel funny!"

Sam took Norman home, but as soon as Sam had gone, Norman made a quick recovery.

"Party time!" he said.

Back at the café, Bella and Mandy were testing the candles.

They lit them then blew them out.

But these were no ordinary candles – when Bella and Mandy went into the kitchen, the flames lit up again!

Meanwhile, Dusty had found
the birthday cake, and tried to lick
a bit of the delicious icing.

Suddenly, the cake slid off the
table and on to the floor setting
the tablecloth on fire!

When Norman arrived at the café, he saw the fire.

"Help! **Fire!**" he cried.

"Mamma mia!" said Bella.
"Everybody out, at once!"

"Action Stations!"

said Station Officer Steele when he heard about the fire.

The alarm bell rang and Sam, Penny and Elvis jumped aboard Jupiter with the blue lights flashing and the siren wailing – **Nee Nah! Nee Nah!** – and they raced off at full speed.

When they arrived at Bella's café, Sam and the crew soon put out the fire and made sure everyone was safe.

Later, Bella made another birthday cake for Sam. At the Fire Station, the party was nearly ready.

Sarah and James had decorated with balloons and streamers.

Mandy had drawn a colourful
birthday card for Sam.

When they were ready, Norman
told everyone to be quiet, while
he called Sam into the gym.

"SURPRISE!" everyone cried. "Happy birthday, Sam!"

Sam was very surprised! "I thought you'd all forgotten," he laughed.

"Of course not, Uncle Sam," said Sarah. "We had to get everything ready in secret."

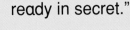

"And it was my job to keep you out of here," said Norman.

"Ah, that explains your odd behaviour today then, Norman!" said Sam.

"Blow out the candles on your cake, Sam," said Elvis.

Sam tried – but the candles lit up again!

"Crikey, Sam," said Norman. "You must be getting old. You haven't got enough puff to blow out your candles!"